# FISHES OF
# BRITAIN'S RIVERS AND LAKES

*by*

## J. R. NORMAN

*Assistant Keeper, British Museum*
*(Natural History)*

*The* KING PENGUIN *Books*
PUBLISHED BY PENGUIN BOOKS LIMITED
LONDON *and* NEW YORK
1943

# THE KING PENGUIN BOOKS

Editor: N. B. L. Pevsner
Technical Editor: R. B. Fishenden

THIS VOLUME PUBLISHED 1943

MADE IN GREAT BRITAIN

*Text Pages printed by*
R. & R. CLARK, LTD., EDINBURGH
Set in Monotype Baskerville

*Colour Plates*
Made and printed by JOHN SWAIN & SON, LTD.

*Cover design by*
CHARLES PAINE

PUBLISHED BY

PENGUIN BOOKS LIMITED
HARMONDSWORTH MIDDLESEX
ENGLAND

PENGUIN BOOKS INC.
245 FIFTH AVENUE
NEW YORK

# TABLE OF CONTENTS

## Introduction

WHAT is a fish? The schoolboy who, when asked this question, replied that 'it swam in the water and had scales and fins' was not far wrong. If we add that it also has a skull and a backbone, a brain and a spinal cord, and that it breathes oxygen dissolved in the water, by means of gills, we shall have a good definition. Salmon, Pike and Perch are fishes; Crayfishes, Mussels and Newts are not.

Thus defined, there are about forty-five different kinds of fresh-water fishes in these islands. Most people will be familiar with at least some of them and are not likely to confuse the three kinds just mentioned, but too often their acquaintance will have been with dead or stuffed specimens, illustrations in books, or with fishes living in an aquarium. Of their life in their natural surroundings, and the ceaseless struggle that they wage for their very existence beneath the surface of every lake, pond and stream, most of us know very little. Nor is this surprising, for the very nature of its native element effectively veils the activities of a fish. Even the angler or the professional fisherman, with better chances of observing fishes than most, sees little more than an occasional dark shadow gliding across the bottom, a slight disturbance of the surface as a fish rises to feed, or a momentary flash of silver as it leaps from the water to escape from its enemies. Nevertheless, there is a story of fish life which is every bit as fascinating as that of the birds or butterflies, and which has been gradually pieced together by patient observation, research and experiment.

One reason for the comparative lack of popular interest in our fishes may be that, with a few notable exceptions, they play a very minor part in filling the nation's larder, even in war-time. It is true that members of the Salmon family such as the Salmon and Trout are valuable food-fishes, and the Char of Windermere (Plate XII A) and

5

the Pollan of Lough Neagh are the objects of commercial fisheries. Eels, Smelt, Shad and even Lampreys are of considerable economic importance, but species like the Pike, Tench, Bream and Perch—the so-called coarse fishes—are rarely used as food. This is not to say that they are inedible: indeed, as far as nutritive value and palatability are concerned, they compare very favourably with marine fishes, and on the Continent are eaten extensively. The somewhat muddy or weedy flavour of the flesh is against them, but this can be overcome by careful cooking, and baked Pike, to mention only one example, provides an excellent dish—'too good', as Izaak Walton remarks, 'for any but Anglers or honest men'. The truth is that our coarse fishes are scarcely numerous enough to make commercial fishing a paying proposition. The total area of all the fresh-waters of England and Wales is little more than 340 square miles, and it has been estimated that this would produce some 2000 tons of fish in an average year—a modest figure compared with the 700,000 tons yielded by our sea fisheries. In earlier days matters were very different, and our ancestors, lacking modern facilities of refrigeration and cheap transport, learned to esteem such fishes as the Pike, Carp and Tench, and the larger country houses nearly all had their private stew-ponds in which fishes were grown and fattened for the table.

## Environment

A glance through the plates in this book, which are reproduced from the originals in Edward Donovan's *Natural History of British Fishes* (see the note on the author on page 23), will show that our own fresh-water fishes present a good deal of variation both in form and coloration, although they lack the fantastic shapes and bizarre colour patterns found among fishes of the tropics. The differences between some of the species are, at all events, sufficiently striking to provoke a query as to their meaning. Why should the Bream (Plate I A) have a deep, compressed and comparatively clumsy body, while its near relative the Dace (Plate III B) shows such slender and graceful proportions? Why is the Dace (Plate III B) silvery and the Tench (Plate I B) more or less olive-coloured? What is the meaning of the conspicuous black bars on the flanks of a Perch (Plate V A)? Why does a Pike (Plate IX B) have powerful jaws and a fearsome array of teeth, and the Sturgeon (Plate IX A) a feeble, toothless mouth? The answer to all these and to other questions of a like nature is to be found in the fish's own surroundings, its environment, to use a scientific term. The diverse shapes and colours of our fishes, as well as their mouths, teeth and other bodily characters, have not been arbitrarily acquired, but have been gradually moulded through countless generations in conformity with the laws of evolution that govern all living organisms. 'Yes,' it may be said: 'we know that land animals are adapted for a particular mode of life. We realise that there are desert animals, forest animals, animals of the steppes and tundras, flying animals and swimming animals, just as there are perching, wading and swimming birds. But all fishes live in water which, apart from being fresh or salt, is much the same everywhere.' This reasoning is unsound. Water is by no means the homogeneous element that it is popularly supposed to be, and the environment of fishes far from uniform. The water may be acid or alkaline, deep or shallow, warm or cold, turbid or clear; it may be stagnant or moving, it may be sluggish or flow swiftly. The river-bed or lake-floor may be composed of clay, chalk, gravel or peat. All these factors go to make up what may be described as the fish's inanimate environment, and play their part, directly or indirectly, in moulding its bodily form.

Looked at in this way, the diversity of form and colour becomes less puzzling. The stately proportions of the Bream (Plate I A) are well suited for life in the lakes and sluggish streams where it abounds, but would be out of place in the clear swiftly-flowing waters favoured by the slender Dace (Plate III B). The streamlined contours of the Salmon, with every inch of its slender, fusiform body admirably adapted for swift progress, are typical of an active predacious fish, equally at home in the sea or swimming against the stream in the rivers. Contrast this fish with the Eel, with its long, cylindrical body; a fish which does comparatively little active swimming, but delights to wriggle through the mud or in and out of holes and crevices. The little Gudgeon (Plate I B), like many other fishes that spend their time on or near the sandy or gravelly river-bed, has the belly flattened rather then rounded. The Flounder (Plate VI A), however, is the bottom-living fish *par excellence*, and its whole body is perfectly adapted to this mode of life. It is compressed like the Bream, but, instead of swimming upright, moves and lies on one of its sides (usually the left), and is unique among our fresh-water fishes in having both its eyes on the same side of the head. Further, the side of the fish which is uppermost is coloured to match the ground on which it lies, while the opposite or blind side remains white.

## Coloration

The colours of fresh-water fishes may be even more diverse than their shapes, and this is true not only of the different species, but sometimes of different individuals of the same species. Generally speaking, all these varied shades and patterns have but one meaning and are designed to render their possessors as inconspicuous as possible in their natural surroundings, and thus to conceal them from their prey or from enemies. With the exception of a few bottom-living forms, all our fresh-water fishes, however diverse their liveries may appear to be, show one general principle of coloration, a principle adopted by many land animals and known to scientists as obliterative shading. Their backs are always darker than their bellies, and they exhibit a gradation of shades from dark blue, green or brown above to silvery or yellowish white beneath. Living as they do in a medium through which light descends upon them from above, this type of shading is exactly the opposite of that produced by the light, and the general effect is to destroy the impression of thickness and to make the fish appear as a perfectly flat object. Many of our species such as the Roach (Plate III A) and Bream (Plate I A) depend entirely upon this simple shading to escape observation, but others enhance the obliterative effect by the addition of darker bars, spots and stripes of all kinds, which tend to break up the outline and obscure the form, besides harmonising with the ground on which they rest or the vegetation among which they swim. Those who have watched a shoal of Perch (Plate V A) moving slowly through a forest of reed-stems, cannot have failed to notice how the disruptive pattern provided by the intense bars on the flanks conceals them to a remarkable degree. It may be noted that young Perch exhibit a coloration more suited for a life near the surface, and only later acquire that of the bottom-dwelling adults.

Where a species normally occupies one type of habitat little variation in the colours or markings is to be expected, but in the Trout, which, in addition to the sea, is also found in lakes, large rivers, streams and mountain tarns, the coloration is very varied. Experiments have shown that individual Trout can change their colours to some extent to match their immediate surroundings, and that, in addition to the nature of the bottom, the amount of light present is an important factor in determining the ground colour and perhaps also the markings. 'Trout with intense ocellated spots', writes the late Dr. Günther, 'are generally found in clear rapid rivers and in small open Alpine pools; in the large lakes with pebbly bottom the fish are bright silvery, and the ocellated spots are mixed with or replaced by X-shaped black spots; in pools or parts of lakes with muddy or peaty bottom the Trout are of a darker colour generally, and when enclosed in caves or holes they may assume an almost uniform blackish coloration.' Trout of mountain tarns are intensely coloured, and often quite black.

The Flounder is unique among our fresh-water fishes

in its capacity for rapid colour changes. Lying half-buried in a patch of river mud, its blackish colour makes it almost invisible while resting, but, let that same fish move onto an area of sand, and, almost at once, its general hues change from black to yellowish brown. Incidentally, it can be shown that this, or any other fish, must be able to *see* its surroundings before it can effect a colour change. A Flounder (Plate VI A) lying with its head on a white ground and the rest of its body on a black ground will remain pale all over, and blind fish or those provided with 'blinkers' usually remain dark even when placed on a white ground. Sometimes colour changes may be associated with emotion, and our little Bull-head has been shown to exhibit different shades with fear, anger, greed and so on. Curiously enough, most fishes assume a dark coloration when alarmed, in contrast with the pallor associated with fear in ourselves.

### Food and Feeding

Such examples of the part played by the environment in moulding the bodies of fishes might be multiplied indefinitely, but it must be borne in mind that the term environment covers a good deal more than the purely physical or inanimate factors already mentioned. Of equal importance are the effects of the animate environment, that is to say, the other animals and the plants with which a fish may be associated in its daily life. Good examples are provided when we consider the correlation between the nature of the food on the one hand and the form of the mouth, teeth and other parts of the fish's anatomy concerned with feeding on the other. The Pike (Plate IX B), with its powerful jaws bristling with sharply-pointed teeth, and with similar teeth on the roof of the mouth and on the tongue, feeds mainly on other fishes, even including its own kind. So insatiable is its appetite and so rapid its digestion, that a Pike is said to consume as much as its own weight of food in a single day! The Perch (Plate V A) is another predacious fish, with a mixed diet in which smaller fishes predominate, and this species also has strong jaws and the teeth sharply pointed. Salmon (fig. 1) and Trout (Plate XI) have a mixed carnivorous diet, and both jaws and teeth are well developed, but the related Whitefish and the Shad (Plate VI B) are plankton feeders, *i.e.* they subsist mainly upon the swarms of minute animals and plants found near the surface. The jaws of these fishes are comparatively feeble and the teeth minute, but a special sieve-like mechanism has been developed in connection with the gills to strain the food from the water. Grey Mullets (Plate XIII B) also have a filtering apparatus which serves to sift the decomposing animal

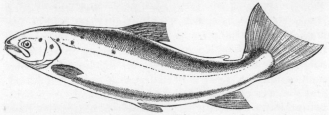

*Figure 1: Salmon*

and vegetable matter, on which they live, from the mud. The teeth are reduced to a mere fringe of tiny bristles, but this unusual diet has had the effect of producing a muscular, gizzard-like stomach and a long closely-coiled intestine. The Sturgeon (Plate IX A), with the habit of rooting about in the sand or mud in search of small animals of all kinds, has a curious circular mouth, quite devoid of teeth, which can be thrust downwards like a funnel and used to suck up the food. All the members of the Carp family have toothless mouths, which in some species can be protruded to a considerable extent. There are, however, a few highly specialised teeth in the throat, which are borne on a pair of strong, sickle-shaped bones and bite against a horny pad at the base of the skull. The form of these pharyngeal teeth varies in the different species in accordance with the diet, which includes a high percentage of vegetable matter. Finally, we have the Lampreys (Plates X B, V B), which have adopted a mode of life which may be described as semi-parasitic. Attaching themselves to other fishes by means of their suctorial, jawless mouths, they rasp the flesh off their living victims with the muscular piston-like tongue armed with horny teeth.

Some fishes have developed special sensory organs round their mouths known as barbels. These have the form of fleshy filaments, and are used mainly as feelers to search for food. The Sturgeon (Plate IX A) has a row of four barbels hanging down from the snout, the Carp (Plate II A) and the Barbel (Plate X A) two pairs attached to the upper lip, the Gudgeon (Plate XVI B) and the Tench (Plate I B) a single pair, and the Loach (Plate VII B) three pairs. The Burbot (Plate XIV B) has a single barbel hanging from the lower jaw. In general, fishes with barbels are to be found living in turbid or deep water and feeding mainly on the bottom. Under such conditions, sight is of little use in seeking for food, and the eyes of these fishes are always small. As a compensation for the reduction in the visual sense, they have these highly sensitive feelers (which may also be provided with taste organs), as well as a much enhanced sense of smell.

### Breeding

Nearly all the activities of a fish so far discussed have been concerned with obtaining food or escaping from natural enemies, and most of the modifications that its body has undergone can be shown to be correlated, directly or indirectly, with one or other of these ends. Once a year, however, these are relegated to secondary importance, and practically the whole of its energies are devoted to reproduction. It is well known that once they leave the sea on their breeding journey Salmon and Trout give up feeding altogether until spawning is over, and other fishes probably feed very little during this all-important time. Most of our species breed in the spring, but Salmon and Trout may spawn at any time from September to February, and the seaward migration of the Eel occurs in late summer and autumn. In nearly all cases breeding involves some sort of journey for the parents—a few hundred yards in the case of a Pike or Bream, perhaps a hundred miles or so in the case of the Salmon, and no less than two thousand miles in the case of the Eel.

Most of our coarse fishes prefer reedy shallows in streams or backwaters, or near the edges of lakes, for spawning, and usually congregate in large shoals at this time. Excitement is intense, and so intent are the fish on the business in hand that they seem oblivious to danger. A large shoal may present an amazing sight, with many of the males sporting at the surface or even leaping clean out of the water. Roach (Plate III A) have been described as massing so closely that the movements of their bodies against each other produced a gentle hissing noise, and at times smaller fish were lifted half out of the water by the passage of larger ones. Often two, three or even more males can be seen in attendance upon a single female, swimming excitedly round and above her, and even pushing her body with their snouts to assist the extrusion of the eggs. The hard, wart-like nuptial tubercles often developed on the head and elsewhere in the males at this season may assist this process.

All the species spawning in fresh water produce what are known as demersal eggs, with a hard and smooth, or sticky outer envelope, which are heavy enough to sink to the bottom. After extrusion, the eggs in some forms sink to the sand or gravel, where they develop, but in others they may be attached to the stems of water plants or other objects. The Perch (Plate V A) produces its eggs in a long floating band, one end of which is attached to the vegetation. Some species make provision for the safety of the eggs by depositing them in crevices, scooping out crude nests for their reception, or by covering them with sand or gravel. The female Salmon makes troughs or 'redds' in gravelly shallows where the stream is fairly rapid, using her body and tail for this operation. In each of these she deposits a few eggs, which are fertilised by the male and afterwards loosely covered. Once the spawning process has been completed, the vast majority of fresh-water fishes take no further interest in the fate of their offspring, and any sort of parental care is the exception rather than the rule. The difficulty of ensuring that most of the eggs are fertilised after extrusion, coupled with the enormous risks of destruction to which the eggs and fry are exposed, makes this rather haphazard method of reproduction a wasteful one, and relatively enormous numbers of eggs are produced by each individual fish to compensate for the prospective loss.

The Bull-head (Plate VII A) and Three-spined Stickleback (Plate VIII A) are good examples of fishes which take their parental duties more seriously and consequently are able to produce fewer eggs. Bull-heads pair in March or April, and then proceed to scoop out a rough nest, usually beneath a stone, in a quiet shallow stretch of water. The eggs adhere to the under side of the stone and the male mounts guard for a month or more, chasing away intruders both large and small. The Three-spined Stickleback constructs an elaborate domed nest out of the roots and stems of water plants, using a secretion from its own kidneys and the mucus coating its body to bind the materials together. This duty is undertaken solely by the male, who then courts one female after another, and conducts each chosen mate to the nest, where she deposits her eggs. When sufficient eggs have been extruded and fertilised in this way, the male takes charge of the nest, which he defends assiduously against all comers until the young are old enough to fend for themselves. Should another Stickleback, or, indeed, any other fish, approach the nest, the devoted father will give battle furiously, chasing away the intruder and often inflicting havoc on him with his sharp spines.

With most fishes spawning is followed by a period of rest and intensified feeding, in which the parents recuperate their strength. In the Salmon and Trout, however, where the journey from the sea may be a lengthy one and the spawning process exhausting, very few males and only a proportion of the females survive to breed a second time. Spent fish, known as kelts, present a sorry appearance, with large ungainly heads and emaciated bodies, and in such a condition fall an easy prey to disease, injuries and to enemies of all kinds. The Salmon of the Pacific coast of America may have to make a journey of more than two thousand miles to the spawning grounds, and here none of the parents ever survives. In some rivers the corpses of spent fish have been seen piled up high on the banks for miles. The Sea Lamprey

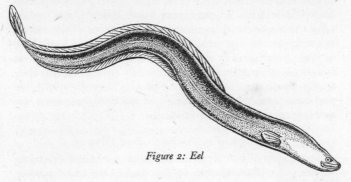

*Figure 2: Eel*

(Plate X B), which also migrates up-river to breed, likewise dies when spawning is completed.

Fishes such as the Salmon, Sea Trout, Shad and Sturgeon, which spend most of their lives in the sea and only ascend the rivers to breed, are known as *anadromous*, in contrast to the *catadromous* Eel, which feeds and grows in fresh water for several years and returns to its original home in the sea to spawn (fig. 2). Every autumn a certain number of adult Eels exchange their normal coloration for a silvery breeding livery, cease to feed, and make their way downstream to the sea, even wriggling across grass at night when dew is heavy in order to reach the nearest river. Once in the sea, they head for the open ocean and make their way to an area in the Western Atlantic south of Bermudas, in which suitable conditions

15

of temperature, salinity and so on for breeding are to be found. As might be expected, such a journey is possible only once in a lifetime, and, after spawning, the parents die. The eggs are buoyant and soon hatch out into tiny, flattened, leaf-like transparent larvae, known as Leptocephalids, which are provided with fine needle-like teeth. These feed on minute organisms, grow rapidly, and, assisted by the Gulf Stream, gradually migrate eastwards, and finally approach the coasts of Europe when about three inches long and a little more than two years old. They now cease to feed and change into little cylindrical elvers or glass-eels, each about two and a half inches in length. These elvers move inshore, and, when about three years old, commence the ascent of the rivers, running up in literally enormous numbers. They will wriggle over weirs or other obstacles, or travel over short stretches of grassland if sufficiently moist, until they finally reach a suitable resting-place. Here they will live and grow until the time comes to start on their own last journey to the breeding-grounds.

### Origin of British Fresh-Water Fishes

The origin of our fresh-water fishes and their distribution in these islands, both to-day and in the more remote past, provides a fascinating problem which can be only briefly summarised here. Those who are interested in the subject should read the chapter on geographical distribution in Dr. Regan's book *The Freshwater Fishes of the British Isles*.

There can be little doubt that the original home of fishes was in the sea, and that the ancestors of our modern fresh-water forms which penetrated into the rivers did so largely to seek for new food supplies, to escape from enemies, and to find suitable quiet spots to breed. Some of these must have become permanent residents in fresh water, and the changed conditions acting very slowly over countless generations would in time tend to produce colonies or races, and, later, species, quite distinct from their marine forebears. Spreading farther and farther away from the sea, these new forms would become progressively more and more modified by their environment, until finally there would be whole families or even higher groups composed entirely of fresh-water fishes, a position which we actually find to-day.

It is common to divide our fresh-water fishes into two primary categories: (1) those that spend part of their lives in the sea, and (2) those that live permanently in fresh water. This distinction is convenient but by no means as clear-cut as would appear. The migratory Sea Trout, feeding and growing in the sea and ascending rivers to breed, belongs to the same species as the purely fluviatile Brown Trout of the rivers or lakes: the coloration may be somewhat different, but there are no structural differences and the young are indistinguishable. Further, the ranks of Sea Trout are probably reinforced from time to time by recruits from the offspring of non-migratory parents, and, conversely, Sea Trout prevented from going to the sea learn to live and breed in fresh water. On the other hand, species such as the Roach and Perch, which would certainly be placed in the second category, are capable of living in brackish water, and both of these species are to be found in parts of the Baltic, as well as in the Caspian Sea, in which the water is more or less salt. It is of interest to note that in general fresh-water fishes seem to be more intolerant of salt water than marine fishes are of fresh, but the degree of intolerance varies in different species. The Norfolk Broads are sometimes flooded by the sea, with disastrous effects on the local fishes, and it has been noticed that the Pike, Tench, Roach and Bream are the first to succumb, the Perch stands a fairly strong admixture of salt, and the Eel is unaffected. The Flounder and the Three-spined Stickleback are equally at home in salt or fresh water, and seem to be able to pass from one to another fairly rapidly without harm.

On the whole, then, it will perhaps be better to define our two main categories in this way: (1) those fishes which either spend a part of their lives in the sea or which have been derived in comparatively recent times from ancestors with this habit; and (2) those fishes that have lived and evolved in fresh water for a long time, and which have reached these islands from Europe as fresh-water fishes. The principal species of the British Isles may then be grouped as follows:

1. Sea Lamprey, River Lamprey, Sturgeon, Shad, Salmon, Trout, Char, Whitefish, Eel, Bass, Grey Mullet, Flounder, Three-spined Stickleback.

2. Planer's Lamprey, Grayling, Pike, Barbel, Gudgeon, Tench, Minnow, Chub, Dace, Roach, Rudd, Bream, Bleak, Loach, Burbot, Perch, Ruffe, Bull-head, Ten-spined Stickleback.

As to the first group, Grey Mullet (Plate XIII B) and Bass (Plate II B) are marine fishes, but commonly frequent estuaries and penetrate into the rivers, especially in the summer months. The Flounder (Plate VI A) is likewise a sea fish, found in shallow water all round Europe, but gets upstream well beyond the influence of the tides. The Three-spined Stickleback (Plate VIII A) is equally at home in sea or river, and has a wide range in the Northern Hemisphere. In these islands it is both marine and fresh-water, in northern regions essentially marine, and in Spain and Italy almost entirely fluviatile. The presence of a fresh-water Three-spined Stickleback in Algeria suggests that at one time the range of the species extended in the sea farther to the south than it does to-day.

Such members of the Salmon family as the Salmon, Trout, Char and Whitefish are believed to have been primarily marine anadromous fishes of arctic and northern seas, and the Salmon and Trout of these islands are probably to be regarded as two very closely related marine species, each with much the same range in the sea and each running up rivers to spawn. At various times both species have founded non-migratory fresh-water colonies, either voluntarily through finding abundance of food and perhaps fewer enemies in the lakes and rivers, or involuntarily through the occurrence of some physical barrier preventing the young fish from getting back to the sea. Colonies of this sort have probably been reinforced from time to time from sea-going stocks. The Salmon has not formed such colonies in these islands, but Lake Wenern in Sweden, now isolated from the sea by impassable falls, and some of the larger lakes and rivers of Quebec, New Brunswick and Maine are renowned for their land-locked Salmon. The Trout, on the other hand, has formed fluviatile colonies in suitable lakes and rivers all over its range, and some of these races have become so distinctive that some authorities have described them as separate species. Actually there is only one species of Trout in the British Isles, which is identical with that of Europe. The present geographical position of some of these fresh-water colonies provides a valuable clue to the range of the species in the sea in earlier times. To-day it occurs as a marine fish from Iceland and the northern part of Norway southwards to the Bay of Biscay, but fresh-water Trout are found in the Atlas Mountains of North Africa, in Corsica and Sardinia, and in some countries north of the Mediterranean. Incidentally, there is a species of fish, distinguished by its small size and feeble mouth, living in the rivers of Albania and Dalmatia, which is structurally very close to our own Salmon. There can be little doubt that the southward range in the sea of both Salmon and Trout is limited by the temperature of the sea itself. During the period in the earth's history known as the Glacial Epoch or Ice Age, when climatic conditions in Europe were colder, both must have occurred in the Mediterranean and spawned in suitable rivers draining into that sea. On the return of a milder climate the migratory fish would have been compelled gradually to retreat northwards, leaving behind the fresh-water colonies.

The fresh-water races of Char and Whitefish, which very rarely occur as sea fish in our islands, have originated in much the same way. The range of the migratory Char is more northerly than that of the Trout, extending southwards in the sea as far as Iceland and the northern coasts of Europe—roughly the northern limit for migratory Trout. During the Glacial Epoch the range of the Char must have extended farther south, and, following this period, the melting of the ice, coupled with gradual elevation of the land, led to the appearance of a number of deep, cold lakes into which Char made their way. The later isolation of these lakes from the sea left stocks of Char in such places as the lakes of Scandinavia, Switzerland, Scotland, the Lake District of England, and North Wales, where they still occur to-day. Such stocks have continued to evolve in various directions and to various degrees in response to the local environment, and such forms as the Windermere Char (Plate IV A), the Torgoch or Welsh Char (Plate IV B), and the Cole's Char of Ireland, are very different-looking fishes from the migratory form from which they have arisen. In just the same way, northern migratory Whitefish seem to have given rise to such land-locked forms as the Vendace, Pollan, Powan, Schelly and Gwyniad, found to-day in the lakes of Britain and Ireland.

The second primary category of British fresh-water fishes includes twenty-two species, all of which occur on the Continent. It is of interest to note that, although a number of them extend eastwards into Asia, and about half have reached Italy, only one has reached Spain—a tribute to the effectiveness of the Pyrenees as a barrier. At the time of the Glacial Epoch Ireland and all but the southernmost part of Britain were lying under a sheet of ice, so that all the species must have reached these islands subsequently—say about 100,000 years ago. When the ice melted, the gradual elevation of the land that followed led to the temporary union of Great Britain and Ireland with each other and with the Continent. This was followed in turn by a subsidence of the land which gave to the British Isles roughly their present shape and boundaries. During the comparatively short period of union it is believed that our eastern and probably also our southern streams were tributaries of large Continental rivers. The eastern streams seem to have formed part of the Rhine, a large stretch of which flowed northwards through what is to-day the bed of the North Sea, while the southern streams were connected with the rivers of northern France through a large river basin which no longer exists. Another large river system linked up the rivers of south-eastern Ireland with those of western England and Wales, including the Severn.

### Dispersal of British Fresh-Water Fishes

If it is a fact that our islands acquired their fresh-water fishes in this manner, we should expect the present distribution of the species to provide at least some corroboration. Dr. Regan has carefully tabulated the twenty-two species, and has shown that all occur in Yorkshire, and nearly all in the Trent, the Ouse, and in Norfolk. There is, however, a marked diminution in the number of species towards the north, with no true indigenous fresh-water fishes in the northern Scottish Highlands, and a similar decrease in number occurs as we go from east to west, with a number of species missing from Wales west of the Severn basin. Only ten species have reached Ireland, a fact which suggests that this island was severed from Britain at an early stage.

The rate at which the subsequent dispersal took place must have varied in different parts of the country, since the spread of fishes would be brought about mainly by such hydrographical changes as the capture by one large river of the tributaries of another, the union of two or more rivers as the result of some geological upheaval, or the joining of two systems, whose headwaters might be only a few miles apart, during abnormal and temporary floods. It has been suggested that the carrying of spawn by waterspouts, or on the feet of aquatic birds, may have accounted for the transference of certain species from one river system to another, but there is no evidence that such accidental methods have played an important part in the dispersal of fresh-water fishes. Man, however, has certainly been responsible for spreading some species, especially those which he esteemed as food. Dr. Regan believes that he must be held in some degree responsible for the present range of the Tench, Pike and Perch, and the extensive stocking of rivers for sporting purposes in modern times will certainly affect the distribution of other species eventually. The Californian Rainbow Trout, and the so-called Brook Trout (really a Char) of Canada and the northern United States, have been introduced into our streams for the benefit of the angler, but in very few waters have either of these fishes become permanently established under normal conditions. Man has also been responsible for the introduction of the Carp (Plate III A), a native of Eastern Asia, into various parts of the world, and for its wide distribution in Britain and Ireland. There is some doubt as to the actual date of its introduction, but it certainly reached our islands several centuries ago. The Gold-fish, which in its native rivers has the greenish and brownish coloration of other Carp-like fishes, is another inhabitant of Asia which has been acclimatised all over the world, and it may be noted that the gold and silver forms, which are merely colour varieties, tend to revert to the ancestral coloration when they escape from artificial waters into the rivers.

# EDWARD DONOVAN
## (1768–1837)

EDWARD DONOVAN devoted his life to the study of natural history, and, being possessed of a considerable private fortune, he was able to amass a large collection of specimens and to publish a number of expensively illustrated books on his favourite subject. In 1807, and for many years afterwards, the public were freely admitted to view his collections, which were exhibited under the title of 'The London Museum and Institute of Natural History' at Brydges Street, Covent Garden. A letter from a Mr. James Parkinson, calling attention to the size and importance of the museum, is printed in the *Philosophical Magazine* for 1807. In his later years Donovan appears to have been in severe financial straits, and in 1833 was forced to publish a memorial concerning his losses at the hands of the booksellers, stating that he had been reduced from affluence almost to ruin and appealing for funds to assist him in litigation.

Donovan's more important works deal with mammals, birds, fishes, shells, insects and other creatures, and were published mainly between 1790 and 1830. The plates reproduced here are from his *Natural History of British Fishes*, the five volumes of which appeared from 1802 to 1808.

Donovan has never been held in high esteem as an author, and William Swainson, writing in 1840, describes him as a 'laborious writer on natural history' and his text as 'verbose and not above mediocrity'. Swainson adds, however, that 'great labour has been bestowed upon the colouring of the plates he published, which renders his works expensive'. Although it must be admitted that some of his coloured drawings of birds and mammals are poorly executed, many of those relating to insects and their life-histories are very good indeed, both as to details and colours. In the *Dictionary of National Biography* we are told that his plates of fishes are 'excellently drawn and their colouring will compare favourably with similar plates in many modern books'. Most readers will agree that the plates selected for reproduction in this little book show considerable artistic merit, and it may be said that in the main the details of the various species are accurate. In certain cases the colours leave something to be desired, possibly because the artist made his painting from a dead and faded fish.

# SOME BOOKS

Iᴛ is impossible to give an adequate list of the numerous books on British fishes, but the following four works may be recommended for further reading. The third of these contains a fuller list of books in the English language dealing with fishes in general, and readers are referred to these for more detailed study.

Dᴀʏ, F., *The Fishes of Great Britain and Ireland*. Two volumes. London, 1880–84.

Jᴇɴᴋɪɴs, J. T., *The Fishes of the British Isles*. London, 1925.

Nᴏʀᴍᴀɴ, J. R., *A History of Fishes*. London, 1931.

Rᴇɢᴀɴ, C. T., *The Freshwater Fishes of the British Isles*. London 1911.

# NOTES ON THE COLOUR PLATES

PLATE I

## (A) BREAM
*Abramis brama* (L.) Family Cyprinidae

Common in lakes and sluggish rivers of England and Ireland, but is absent from Scotland north of the Forth, from western Wales, and from some of our south-western counties. Bream of more than 12 lb. have been taken by anglers. Forms a hybrid with the Roach, known as the Pomeranian Bream.

## (B) TENCH
*Tinca tinca* (L.) Family Cyprinidae

Found all over Europe, in Asia Minor and western Siberia, the Tench prefers still and weedy waters. Sometimes called 'Doctor Fish', because the slime covering its body was said to have curative properties for other fishes. Rarely exceeds 8 lb. in weight.

PLATE II

## (A) CARP
*Cyprinus carpio* (L.) Family Cyprinidae

A native of Eastern Asia, but has been introduced all over the world and is now widely distributed in the British Isles. The Carp of our own waters are probably the descendants of fish originally introduced by the monks and cultivated by them for centuries.

## (B) BASS
*Morone labrax* (L.) Family Serranidae

Most abundant on our southern coasts, and in the summer months commonly enters estuaries and rivers. A great favourite with the angler, the Bass attains to a length of 3 feet or more and a weight of nearly 30 lb. It was much esteemed by the Romans for the table.

PLATE III

## (A) ROACH
### *Rutilus rutilus* (L.) Family Cyprinidae

One of the commonest of fresh-water fishes, but is rare in Cornwall, Devon and West Wales and absent in northern Scotland and Ireland. It prefers lakes or rivers and canals where the stream is not too rapid, and is generally to be seen in shoals. Rarely exceeds a weight of 3 lb., and one weighing 3 lb. 14 oz. taken in a reservoir at Hampton may be regarded as an exceptional fish.

## (B) DACE
### *Leuciscus leuciscus* (L.) Family Cyprinidae

Common in the rivers of England and Wales, except in the west, but absent from Scotland. It is found in the River Blackwater in Ireland, but there is some doubt whether the species is indigenous to that country. A smaller fish than the Roach, the record for rod-and-line is $1\frac{1}{2}$ lb.

PLATE IV

## (A) BLEAK
### *Alburnus alburnus* (L.) Family Cyprinidae

Found all over Europe north of the Alps and Pyrenees. In England it is widely distributed, except in the west, but it is absent from Scotland and Ireland. Prefers shallow and swiftly-flowing rivers. Rarely exceeds a length of 8 inches. The silvery scales are used in the manufacture of artificial pearls.

## (B) POPE or RUFFE
### *Acerina cernua* (L.) Family Percidae

A small member of the Perch family, rarely exceeding a length of 7 or 8 inches. Widely distributed on the Continent, but in these islands found only in the southern and midland districts of England, where it frequents slowly-moving rivers, canals and lakes, and lives mainly on the bottom.

PLATE V

## (A) PERCH
### *Perca fluviatilis* (L.) Family Percidae

Probably one of the best known and most handsome of our fresh-water fishes. It is common in rivers, lakes and ponds nearly all over the British Isles, and is a great favourite with the angler. Normally grows to a weight of 4 or 5 lb., but a fish weighing 5 lb. 4¾ oz. was taken by an angler in Norfolk in 1936.

## (B) LAMPERN OR RIVER LAMPREY
### *Lampetra fluviatilis* (L.) Family Petromyzonidae

Most River Lampreys spend the greater part of their lives in the sea, and ascend the rivers to spawn, but others appear to spend the whole of their lives in fresh water. In this country it is especially abundant in such rivers as the Severn, Trent, Ouse and Dee. It is much more common than the Sea Lamprey, but rarely exceeds a length of 15 inches.

PLATE VI

## (A) FLOUNDER
### *Platichthys flesus* (L.) Family Pleuronectidae

Common all round the British coasts, and ascends all suitable rivers, sometimes well beyond the influence of the tides. Feeds voraciously in fresh water, mainly upon worms, shellfish and crustaceans, and descends to the sea to spawn. The specimen figured is abnormally coloured, and was caught in the Thames.

## (B) ALLIS SHAD
### *Alosa alosa* (L.) Family Clupeidae

A member of the Herring family, and found on the Atlantic coast of Europe as well as in the Mediterranean. Enters rivers in the spring to spawn. Rare in the British Isles, except in the Severn and Shannon. The average weight is less than 4 lb., but examples of 8 lb. have been recorded. The other British species, the Twaite Shad, is smaller.

PLATE VII

## (A) BULL-HEAD or MILLER'S THUMB
### *Cottus gobio* (L.) Family Cottidae

Common throughout England and Wales, preferring clear
brooks or the edges of lakes where the bottom is sandy or
gravelly. It is seldom seen, owing to its habit of hiding under
stones. Rarely exceeds a length of 3 or 4 inches, but specimens
of 6 inches have been recorded. Its flattened head is held to
resemble in shape the thumb of the flour-miller of earlier days.

## (B) LOACH or STONE LOACH
### *Nemacheilus barbatula* (L.) Family Cobitidae

Widely distributed in the British Isles, except in northern
Scotland, the Loach prefers small clear streams with a bed of
gravel or sand. Its diet consists of worms, crustaceans and
other forms of minute life, and feeding takes place mainly at
night, the fish spending the day concealed beneath a stone.
Rarely exceeds a length of 4 or 5 inches.

PLATE VIII

## (A) THREE-SPINED STICKLEBACK
### *Gasterosteus aculeatus* (L.) Family Gasterosteidae

This little fish, so popular with juvenile anglers, swarms in
shoals in ponds and streams all over the British Isles. It is
equally at home in brackish or even in salt water. In the
breeding season the male assumes a brilliant red colour on
the under parts of his body. Rarely exceeds a length of 3 or
4 inches.

## (B) TEN-SPINED STICKLEBACK
### *Pygosteus pungitius* (L.) Family Gasterosteidae

This species has much the same distribution as the Three-
spined Stickleback, but does not appear to extend northwards
in these islands beyond Loch Lomond and the Forth, and is
rare in Ireland. It is a smaller fish, the maximum length being
about 3 inches.

PLATE IX

## (A) STURGEON

*Acipenser sturio* (L.) Family Acipenseridae

Occurs on the coasts of Europe and eastern North America. Does not breed in our rivers, but has been taken in the Severn and Trent. Attains to a length of 18 feet. The roe of the Sturgeon provides caviare, and the air-bladder isinglass. It is a 'royal' fish and the prerogative of the Crown.

## (B) PIKE

*Esox lucius* (L.) Family Esocidae

Found all over Europe, extends eastwards into Asia, and also occurs in North America. There are many records of Pike between 40 and 50 lb., the largest coming from Ireland, and it is likely that it attains an even greater size.

PLATE X

## (A) BARBEL

*Barbus barbus* (L.) Family Cyprinidae

Found in the Danube, Rhine and other rivers of Central Europe. In England it is well known in the Thames and Trent, where it is a favourite with anglers, but elsewhere it occurs only in some Yorkshire rivers. It is usually found in deep streams with a strong flow of water and a pebbly bottom. It grows to a length of 3 feet and a weight of about 20 lb.

## (B) SEA LAMPREY

*Petromyzon marinus* (L.) Family Petromyzonidae

Occurs in the Mediterranean and Atlantic and enters rivers for spawning in Europe and North America. Reaches a length of about 3 feet. The name *Petromyzon*, derived from two Greek words meaning 'stone' and 'to suck', refers to the habit of attaching itself to stones by the sucker-like mouth.

PLATE XI

## (A) BROWN TROUT or RIVER TROUT
### *Salmo trutta* (L.) Family Salmonidae

This is the non-migratory form, which spends all its life in fresh water. The fish illustrated is a very large male, 39 inches long, which was taken from the Thames near Hampton early in the nineteenth century. The form of the jaws and the coloration are typical of a breeding cock-fish.

## (B) SEA TROUT
### *Salmo trutta* (L.) Family Salmonidae

This fish illustrates the typical coloration of a migratory Trout as it arrives from the sea to spawn. Sea Trout of Ireland, Wales and the western coasts of Britain are known as Sewen, under which name they appear in Donovan's work. As spawning approaches a great deal of the shapely brilliance of the fresh-run fish is lost.

PLATE XII

## (A) WINDERMERE CHAR
### *Salvelinus alpinus* (L.) Family Salmonidae

The fish depicted is the Windermere or Willoughby's Char, found in Windermere and other lakes of the Lake District. These fishes are netted in Windermere in considerable numbers, and the local 'potted char' are much esteemed as a delicacy. Attains to a weight of about 3 lb., although the average size is considerably less.

## (B) TORGOCH or WELSH CHAR
### *Salvelinus alpinus* (L.) Family Salmonidae

Char are found in a number of deep, cold lakes of Scotland, Ireland, the Lake District and northern Wales, and, although they vary greatly according to the locality, are regarded as pertaining to a single species. The fish figured is the Torgoch —a Welsh name meaning 'red belly'. It is found only in two or three lakes near Llanberis and in one lake in Merionethshire.

PLATE XIII

## (A) GRAYLING
### *Thymallus thymallus* (L.) Family Salmonidae

An entirely fresh-water member of the Salmon family, this beautifully coloured fish is locally abundant in England and Wales, preferring swiftly-running streams with plenty of water and a stony or rocky bottom. The species has been introduced into Scotland, but is absent from Ireland.

## (B) THICK-LIPPED GREY MULLET
### *Mugil chelo* Cuv. Family Mugilidae

The Grey Mullets frequent bays and estuaries in temperate and tropical seas, and often enter rivers in the summer. The species figured is the commonest of the three found on our coasts. It attains to a length of 3 feet and a weight of nearly 15 lb. Ranges from Scandinavia to the Mediterranean.

PLATE XIV

## (A) SMELT OR SPARLING
### *Osmerus eperlanus* (L.) Family Osmeridae

A marine fish, which enters rivers to spawn. Occurs in vast shoals in some of our rivers, especially in the Forth and the Conway. Rarely exceeds a length of 12 inches. A valuable food fish, and freshly-caught specimens have an odour very similar to that of cucumbers. The name Smelt is probably derived from the Anglo-Saxon *smeolt*, meaning smooth and shining.

## (B) BURBOT
### *Lota lota* (L.) Family Gadidae

This is the only fresh-water member of the Cod family, which includes so many important marine food fishes. It was formerly believed to be confined to rivers flowing into the North Sea in these islands, but has recently been recorded from the Severn. An 8-lb. Burbot from the Trent seems to be the largest British specimen, but elsewhere the species grows to a much greater size.

PLATE XV

## (A) RUDD
*Scardinius erythrophthalmus* (L.) Family Cyprinidae

Locally distributed in England and Wales, and absent altogether from Scotland. Unlike the Roach, however, it has reached Ireland, where it is abundant everywhere. Prefers weedy places in lakes and sluggish rivers, and feeds mainly on the bottom on worms, insect larvae and so on. Attains to a length of about 18 inches. Also known as Red-eye.

## (A) CHUB
*Squalius cephalus* (L.) Family Cyprinidae

Generally distributed in Britain south of the Firth of Forth, but is absent from western Wales, Devon and Cornwall. It does not occur in Ireland. In this country it grows to a length of about 2 feet and a weight of 8 lb. A fish caught on rod and line in the Hampshire Avon weighed 8 lb. 4 oz.

PLATE XVI

## (A) MINNOW
*Phoxinus phoxinus* (L.) Family Cyprinidae

One of the commonest of our fresh-water fishes, and found in streams and lakes all over the British Isles except in northern Scotland. In Ireland its distribution is local. It feeds mainly upon minute crustaceans and insect larvae, and large shoals can be seen searching for food among the stones at the bottom of a clear stream. Rarely exceeds a length of 4 inches.

## (B) GUDGEON
*Gobio gobio* (L.) Family Cyprinidae

A gregarious fish, usually found in rivers, preferring places with a sandy or gravelly bottom. It is generally distributed in England and Wales, except in the Lake District, western Wales and Cornwall. It is common in Ireland, but absent altogether from Scotland. Rarely exceeds a length of 6 to 8 inches.

*Bream*

*Tench*

Carp

Bass

*Roach*

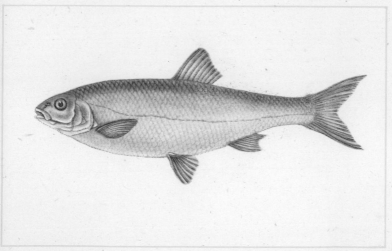

*Dace*

*Bleak*

*Pope or Ruffe*

*Perch*

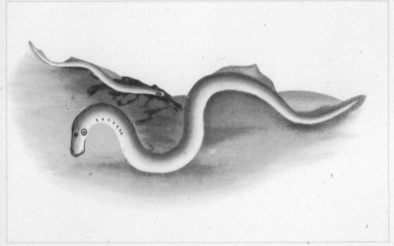

*Lampern or River Lamprey*

*Flounder*

*Allis Shad*

*Bull-head*

*Loach*

*Three-spined Stickleback*

*Ten-spined Stickleback*

*Sturgeon*

*Pike*

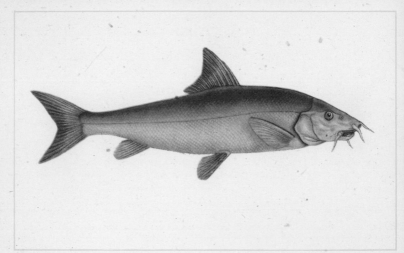

*Barbel*

*Sea Lamprey*

*River or Brown Trout*

*Sea Trout*

*Windermere Char*

*Torgoch or Welsh Char*

Grayling

Grey Mullet

*Smelt*

*Burbot*

*Rudd*

*Chub*

*Minnow*

*Gudgeon*